The London Ripieno Society

PRESIDENT: LADY BARBIROLLI
FOUNDER AND DIRECTOR: GEOFFREY HANSON

presents

AN ENGLISH GARLAND

Four Madrigals:
  Come Again! Sweet Love   *John Dowland (1591-1641)*
  Adieu, Sweet Amaryllis   *John Wilbye (1574-1638)*
  The Silver Swan   *Orlando Gibbons (1583-1625)*
  All Creatures Now   *John Benet (16th century)*
Ave Verum Corpus   *William Byrd (1543-1623)*
I was glad   *Henry Purcell (1659-1695)*
Remember not, Lord, our Offences   "
Organ solo - Geoffrey Hanson:
  Concerto in G Minor   *Matthew Camidge (1784-1844)*
The Blue Bird   *Charles V. Stanford (1852-1924)*
Serenade   *Edward Elgar (1857-1934)*
Great is the Lord   "

I N T E R V A L

Hymn to the Virgin   *Benjamin Britten (1913-1976)*
Now Welcom Somer   *Geoffrey Hanson (b.1939)*
Beside the Idle Summer Sea   "
Set me as a Seal   *William Walton (1902-1983)*
Salve Regina   *Herbert Howells (1892-1983)*
Organ solo - Gary Eyre:
  Flourish for a Bidding   "
Linden Lea   *R. Vaughan Williams (1872-1958)*
Country Gardens   *Cecil Sharp, arr. Henry Geehl*
We'll Gather Lilacs   *Ivor Novello (1893-1951)*
Organ solo - Gary Eyre:
  Carol (in memory of Delius)   *Percy Whitlock (1903-1946)*
Valiant for Truth   *Ralph Vaughan Williams*

Gary Eyre, *organ, with*

The London Ripieno Singers

conducted by **GEOFFREY HANSON**

St. Bride's Church, Fleet Street, London EC4
29 June 1995

This concert is given with financial assistance from MIDLAND BANK PLC

EINLEITUNG

Henry Purcell komponierte in der Zeit von etwa 1677 bis zu seinem Tod im Jahre 1695 einige zur Aufführung in der Royal Chapel und in Westminster Abbey gedachte Werke, die zu den Meisterwerken der englischen Musik überhaupt gehören. Es sind dies nicht nur einige der bedeutendsten, sondern auch der ausdrucksvollsten und einfallsreichsten Werke englischer Musik; auf uns gekommen sind mehr als hundert Anthems und für Andachtszwecke geschriebene Lieder. Aus diesem Repertoire werden in der vorliegenden Ausgabe fünf Anthems vorgelegt, die überwiegend für gemischten Chor geschrieben sind und wohl zwischen 1680 und 1685 entstanden.

Zur Aufführung

Stimmung: Der in der Royal Chapel zu Purcells Zeit gebräuchliche Stimmton lag wohl etwas höher als heutzutage. Ein Stimmton von 466 Hz (einen Halbton über der heute gebräuchlichen Stimmung) entspricht wohl am ehesten der Intonation Purcells, eine Ausführung mit 440 Hz (moderne Stimmung) ist aber ebenfalls möglich und wird die strahlenden Klangfarben von Purcells Musik zur Geltung bringen.

Stil: Purcells Kompositionen waren stark von den neuesten zeitgenössischen Kompositionsrichtungen des Kontinents beeinflußt, vor allem von der italienischen Musik. Bei der Aufführung sollte nicht außer acht gelassen werden, daß es sich um eine leidenschaftliche Kompositionsweise handelt, bei der Affekte und Stimmungen durch recht gewagte Melodien und Harmonien ausgedrückt werden. Die Anthems sollten mit starkem Ausdruck interpretiert werden, wobei Höhepunkte auf jeden Fall deutlich herausgearbeitet werden sollten. *Hear my prayer* beispielsweise besteht im Grunde aus einem Crescendo, das vom Anfang des Stückes zum Schluß hin entwickelt wird und in einem mächtigen Disakkord zu Beginn des vorletzten Taktes gipfelt.

Continuo-Aussetzung: Außer bei dem Anthem *Jehova*, bei dem die linke Hand der Orgelstimme von Purcell stammt, ist der komplette Continuo-Part für das Tasteninstrument eine herausgeberische Ergänzung (auch die Bezifferung). Die Begleitung durch Orgel bietet sich an, für dieses Instrument wurde die Continuo-Aussetzung auch konzipiert. Erfahrene Continuo-Spieler werden natürlich ihre eigene Aussetzung spielen. Die Bezifferung entspricht der harmonischen Struktur des Ganzen (d.h. unter Einschluß der Singstimmen) und wird nicht notwendigerweise durch die gedruckte Aussetzung in der rechten Hand komplett wiedergegeben. Die ausgearbeitete Stimme soll dem weniger erfahrenen Spieler eine stilistisch korrekte Variante bieten, die in den meisten Fällen ohne weitere Ergänzungen spielbar sein dürfte. Bei den Anthems *Jehova* und *Lord how long* ist die Begleitung durch ein Tasteninstrument zwingend notwendig; die anderen drei Anthems könnten ohne Begleitung aufgeführt werden, klingen aber doch mit Orgelbegleitung besser. Ein gestrichenes Baß-Instrument (Cello, Viola da gamba oder – für den wahren Perfektionisten – Baß-Violine) ist eine hervorragende Ergänzung, genauso wie eine Theorbe oder eine Erzlaute. Falls solche Instrumente verfügbar sind, sollten die groß gestochenen Noten der Baßlinie des Continuo-Parts wiedergegeben werden; bei den Stellen ohne solche Noten in Normalstich und ohne Bezifferung sollte die Orgel allein weiterspielen, und zwar in der Regel einen "basso seguente", der die Klangfarben der Vokalstimmen leicht abschattiert.

Zur Edition

Alle dynamischen Hinweise, Satzbezeichnungen und und Verzierungen sind Zutat des Herausgebers. Eckige Klammern über dem Liniensystem bei einigen Kadenzen weisen auf vom Herausgeber gekennzeichnete Hemiolen hin; es sollte hierbei allerdings beachtet werden, daß die Hemiolenbildung an solchen Stellen nicht notwendigerweise alle Stimmen betrifft, und daß Hemiolen auch nicht bei jedem möglichen Vorkommen gekennzeichnet sind. Die Hinweise des Herausgebers dienen der Anleitung der Ausführenden und sollten keineswegs so verstanden werden, als sei die Interpretation dieses Herausgebers die einzig denkbare Lösung. Verzierungen sollten immer auf der oberen Nebennote beginnen und mit einem langen Vorschlag ausgeführt werden. Der eigentliche Triller ist relativ kurz. Bei der Ausführung ist es den Chören freigestellt, Triller wegzulassen oder weitere Triller zu ergänzen. Taktarten und Notenwerte wurden dem heute Gebräuchlichen angeglichen. Purcell achtete sorgfältig darauf, Akzidentien vor jede alterierte Note zu setzen. Diese nach unseren Notationsvorschriften zum Teil überflüssigen Akzidentien wurden entfernt, während Akzidentien, die der Herausgeber für notwendig hielt, ohne weitere Kennzeichnung ergänzt wurden. Die Werke wurden in jedem Fall entweder nach Purcells autographem Manuskript oder aus der verläßlichsten zeitgenössischen Quelle ediert.

COMMENTARY

Choirs performing any of these works in concerts using this edition may reproduce the commentaries below as programme notes, provided credit is given to the author ('Notes © 1994 Robert King').

For the opulent Coronation of James II on 23 April 1685 Purcell composed two new anthems. For the entrance of the King and Queen at the start of the service he wrote a new setting of Psalm 122, **I was glad when they said unto me**. Sandford reports that 'the King and Queen being entered the Church, were received by the Dean and Prebendaries, who, with the Choir of Westminster, proceeding a little before Their Majesties, sung the full Anthem following', and added in his margin that the anthem was 'Composed by Mr. Hen. Purcel, a Gentleman of the Chapel Royal, and Organist of St Margarets Westminster'. James Hawkins, the eighteenth century compiler of the Ely Manuscript now held in the Cambridge University Library, mistakenly ascribed the anthem to John Blow, and it is only fairly recently that its authorship has been restored to Purcell.

The opening is suitably celebratory, using rich five-part harmony and joyful dotted figurations for the word 'glad'. The tribes of the Lord appear one by one as they congregate from their various corners, joining in homophony as they 'give thanks unto the name of the Lord'. At 'O pray for the peace of Jerusalem' the mood alters to one of supplication before the lighter, triple-time metre returns with the hope that peace and plenteousness will bless the royal palaces. The Gloria begins exultantly, with the opening word repeated three times: at 'as it was in the beginning' Purcell returns to imitation, but he saves his compositional tour-de-force for 'world without end': the imitative point (a four note descending scale) is first treated conventionally, then in inversion (rising), then in inverted augmentation in the bass line (rising at half speed), and finally, as the trebles and altos contest the theme at the original speed in real and inverted form, the tenors take over the single inverted augmentation, and simultaneously the basses triumphantly halve even this speed to present Purcell's theme in double augmentation.

The five-part full anthem **Remember not, Lord, our offences** (dating from around 1680) is a masterpiece. Purcell's use of harmony and discord, his startlingly effective word-setting and his mastery of drama are all magnificently demonstrated in a short piece. The atmosphere is created with the very first word, set as a simple block chord, and then reiterated as the phrase moves forward to 'offences': the first phrase of text is repeated again, still in homophonic style, but this time in the relative major. The first touches of counterpoint appear at 'nor th'offences of our forefathers', and the tension begins to increase with 'neither take thou vengeance of our sins', always countered in at least one voice with the rising phrase 'but spare us good Lord'. Gradually the calls for mercy, to 'spare us', begin to dominate, and the chromaticism and daring use of discord increases: the music climaxes with a desperate plea, 'spare us, good Lord'. Quickly the mood returns to supplication: Purcell's harmony relaxes deliciously onto 'redeem'd' and the tenors' dominant seventh clashes exquisitely with a second inversion chord on 'precious'. It is the tenors again who have a wonderfully subtle inner line at 'for ever' and, after such passion, the anthem ends, as it began, with a calm prayer for salvation.

Lord, how long wilt thou be angry? is contained in Purcell's autograph manuscript now held in the Fitzwilliam Museum (MS 88), but also appears in a number of other sources, suggesting that it was quite widely performed. The opening chorus, set in five parts, is a quietly empassioned prayer which makes a feature of a diminished fourth onto 'long' and rich harmony for 'jealousy'. The verse 'O remember not' is scored for an ATB trio, and leads into the declamatory, homophonic section 'Help us, O God' and the more supplicatory 'O deliver us': the countermelody 'O be merciful unto our sins' provides contrast in its rising chromaticism. The final section 'So we, that are thy people' moves into triple metre, lilting in confident mood.

Jehova, quam multi sunt hostes mei is one of only two sacred Latin motets by Purcell which, from its autograph manuscript, has been dated around 1680. It is not known why Purcell should have set a Latin Psalm text: it is highly improbable that such a work could have been performed at the Anglican Chapel Royal. It is just possible that it could have been written for the catholic chapel of King Charles' Queen Catherine. 'Jehova' is one of Purcell's most astonishing church works, combining progressive and conservative styles. Its declamatory solo and choral work shows Purcell at his most highly Italianate, but combines such forward-looking techniques with sections of polyphony which look back to the English masters of the late renaissance. Harmonically the work shows Purcell at his most adventurous: Elgar is said to have enquired, when orchestrating 'Jehova', whether the score he was using contained misprints! The first section demonstrates Purcell's choral mastery: over the mysterious opening chords the second trebles float their high entry, building towards the angry 'Quam multi insurgent contra me' and the counterpoint of 'quam multi dicunt de anima mea'. The entries of 'non est salus isti in Deo' ('There is no help for him in God') build magnificently to a climax. The tenor solo 'At tu, Jehova' is highly Italianate in its declamation, moving into a section of triple-time arioso: the choir answer with the forceful 'Voce mea ad Jehovam clamanti' and a contrapuntal section 'respondit mihi' which builds to another sumptuous

close, in which the choir basses divert from the continuo line to add extra richness to the harmony. 'Ego cubui et dormivi' is one of Purcell's most vividly atmospheric pieces of choral writing, illustrating the Psalmist sleeping and awaking, safe in the knowledge that the Lord was sustaining him. Purcell splendidly sets the warlike 'Non timebo a myriadibus populi' for solo bass, calling on God to save him. The continuo line at 'Qui percussisti omnes inimicos meos maxilliam' falls inexorably before the teeth of the ungodly are broken. The closing chorus is triumphant in its lilting triple metre.

Jehova, quam multi sunt hostes mei.
Quam multi insurgent contra me.
Quam multi dicunt de anima mea,
Non est ulla salus isti in Deo plane.
At tu, Jehova, clypeus es circa me;
Gloria mea, et extollens caput meum.
Voce mea ad Jehovam clamanti,
Respondit mihi e monte sanctitatis suae maximae.
Ego cubui et dormivi; ego expergefeci me;
Quia Jehova sustentat me.
Non timebo a myriadibus populi,
Quas circum disposuerint metatores contra me.
Surge, surge Jehova; fac salvum me deus mi;
Qui percussisti omnes inimicos meos maxilliam,
Dentes improborum confregisti.
Jehova est salus: super populum tuum,
Sit benedictio tua maxime.

Lord how are they increased that trouble me.
Many are they that rise up against me.
Many there be which say of my soul,
There is no help for him in God.
But thou, O Lord, are a shield for me;
My glory, and the lifter up of my head.
I cried unto the Lord with my voice,
And he heard me out of his holy hill.
I laid me down and slept; I awaked;
For the Lord sustained me.
I will not be afraid of ten thousands of people
That have set themselves against me round about.
Arise, O Lord; save me, O my God:
For thou hast smitten all mine enemies upon the cheek-bone;
Thou hast broken the teeth of the ungodly.
Salvation belongeth unto the Lord:
Thy blessing is upon thy people.

Hear my prayer, O Lord is part of a larger piece that Purcell seemingly failed to complete. The anthem is the last item in the autograph manuscript held in Cambridge's Fitzwilliam Museum, after which come a number of blank pages. Purcell's barline at the end of the manuscript (going through the staves and not through the intervening spaces) is the type which usually indicates another section is to follow: indeed he usually marks the end of a piece with an elaborate flourish. Nonetheless, dating from 1680-82 and setting the first verse of Psalm 102 in eight parts, this is one of the great masterpieces of English church music. With a despairing text and large vocal forces at his disposal, Purcell's imagination was raised to its highest level, yet the melodic material is, on its own, quite simple. The first phrase 'Hear my prayer, O Lord' uses just two melancholy notes a minor third apart, but it is the turning chromaticism of 'crying' that gives the scope for such plangency. The harmonic language, always (after the opening phrases) in at least six parts, is exceptional, even for Purcell, but the most extraordinary feature of the anthem is the build-up which Purcell orchestrates from the outset – here is an inexorable vocal crescendo lasting over three minutes, culminating on a monumental discord on the last repetition of 'come'.

Robert King
London, May 1994

I was glad when they said unto me

Words: Psalm 122, vv. 1, 4–7

See Introduction.
Siehe Einleitung.

Remember not, Lord, our offences

Words: from the Litany

*See Introduction.
Siehe Einleitung.

Lord, how long wilt thou be angry?

Words: Psalm 79, vv. 5, 8, 9, 13

*See Introduction.
Siehe Einleitung.

Jehova, quam multi sunt hostes mei

Words: Psalm 3

*See Introduction.
Siehe Einleitung.*

* [ ] delete *ad lib.*

Hear my prayer, O Lord

Words: Psalm 102, v. 1

*See Introduction. *Siehe Einleitung.*
Note: "pray-er" is set as two syllables by Purcell, but the
syllabic change should be almost imperceptible.

Choral Programme Series

For mixed voices:

Benjamin Britten – Christ's Nativity SATB (div)

Anton Bruckner – Six Sacred Choruses SATB/organ or piano

Antonín Dvořák – Four choruses for mixed voices Op 29 SATB

French Chansons – Saint-Saëns/Fauré/Debussy SATB & SATB/piano

Gustav Holst – Five Partsongs Op 12 SATB

Felix Mendelssohn – Four Sacred Partsongs SATB (div)

C.H.H. Parry – Seven Partsongs SATB

Henry Purcell – Five Anthems SATB/keyboard

Franz Schubert – Four Partsongs SATB/keyboard

C.V. Stanford – Seven Partsongs SATB

Ralph Vaughan Williams – Three Choral Hymns SATB/organ or piano

Giuseppe Verdi – Choruses from 'Il Trovatore', 'Nabucco' and 'Aida' SATB (div)/piano

Gilbert & Sullivan – Opera Choruses 1 SATB/keyboard

Gilbert & Sullivan – Opera Choruses 2 SATB/keyboard

Five English Folksongs (arr. Runswick) SATB

Five American Folksongs (arr. Runswick) SATB

A Gospel Christmas – Spirituals for the festive season (arr. Runswick) SATB/piano

Schwartz – Gospel choruses from 'Godspell' and 'Children of Eden' SATB/piano

Lloyd Webber – Memory and other choruses from 'Cats' SATB/piano

Lloyd Webber – Mr Mistoffelees and other choruses from 'Cats' SATB/piano

For upper voices:

Fauré & Saint-Saëns – Six Motets SA/organ or piano

Franz Schubert – Three Partsongs SSAA/piano

Robert Schumann – Eight Partsongs SA/piano & SSA/piano

English Edwardian Partsongs SA/piano & SSA/piano

Schwartz – Choruses from 'Godspell' and 'Children of Eden' SSA/piano

Lloyd Webber – Memory and other choruses from 'Cats' SSA/piano

Lloyd Webber – Mr Mistoffelees and other choruses from 'Cats' SSA/piano

Faber Music 3 Queen Square London WC1N 3AU

ISBN 0-571-5151

9 780571 515151